Snappy Learner

Handwriting

ages 5-7

www.alligatorbooks.co.uk

Published in 2017 by Alligator Products Limited, 2nd Floor, 314 Regents Park Road, London N3 2JX

Printed in China.0588

Weave the web

Practise your tracing skills by drawing around the spider and each line of its web.

Fly around

Carefully trace the lines around the butterfly with your pencil.
Colour the picture with your favourite colours.

Stick your Snappy Learner sticker here.

Well done!

Excellent! Stick a star sticker on your reward chart.

Straight and curved letter shapes

Use a pencil to trace the lines of these letters. Then write the letters on the line underneath.

i i i i i i i i i

l l l l l l l l l

t t t t t t t t t

h h h h h h h h h

Excellent! Stick a star sticker on your reward chart.

More straight and curved letters

Use a pencil to trace the lines of these letters. Then write the letters on the line underneath.

w w w w w w w w

v v v v v v v v v

j j j j j j j j j j

Stick your Snappy Learner sticker here.

Well done!

Excellent! Stick a star sticker on your reward chart.

Round and round we go

All of these letter shapes are circular. Use a pencil to trace the lines of these letters. Then write the letters on the line underneath.

o o o o o o o o

a a a a a a a a

c c c c c c c c

g g g g g g g g g

e e e e e e e e
d d d d d d d d
q q q q q q q q
Stick your Snappy Learner sticker here.
Well done!
Excellent! Stick a star sticker on your reward chart.

This way, that way!

All of these letter shapes change direction. Use a pencil to trace the lines of these letters. Then write the letters on the line underneath.

f f f f f f f f f

k k k k k k k k k

x x x x x x x x x

Excellent! Stick a star sticker on your reward chart.

Capital letters

These are all the **capital** letters of the alphabet. Use a pencil to trace around the dotted lines. Then write the letters on the line underneath.

NN OO PP QQ
RR SS TT UU VV
WW XX YY ZZ
Stick your Snappy Learner sticker here.
Well done!
Excellent! Stick a star sticker on your reward chart.

The small case letters

These are all the **small case** letters of the alphabet. Use a pencil to trace around the dotted lines. Then write the letters on the line underneath.

aaa bbb ccc ddd

eee fff ggg hhh iii

jjj kkk lll mmm

nnn ooo ppp qqq

rrr sss ttt uuu vvv

www xxx yyy zzz

Stick your Snappy Learner sticker here.

Well done!

Excellent! Stick a star sticker on your reward chart.

Join the letters up!

Now that you've practised your writing, it is time to join up the letters. Use your pencil to trace over the joined letters on each line without stopping. Then write the joined-up letters yourself on the line underneath.

oo

aa

rr

Stick your Snappy Learner sticker here.
Well done!
Excellent! Stick a star sticker on your reward chart.

Top & bottom

Joined-up writing means joining one letter to the next. This is done by drawing exit strokes at the top or bottom of a letter. Trace the lines to join up all these letters.

at atatatatatatatat

car carcarcarcarcar

too tootootootoo

Loopy letters

These letters can be joined with a loop or left unjoined. Trace the letters and then write the letter yourself on the line underneath.

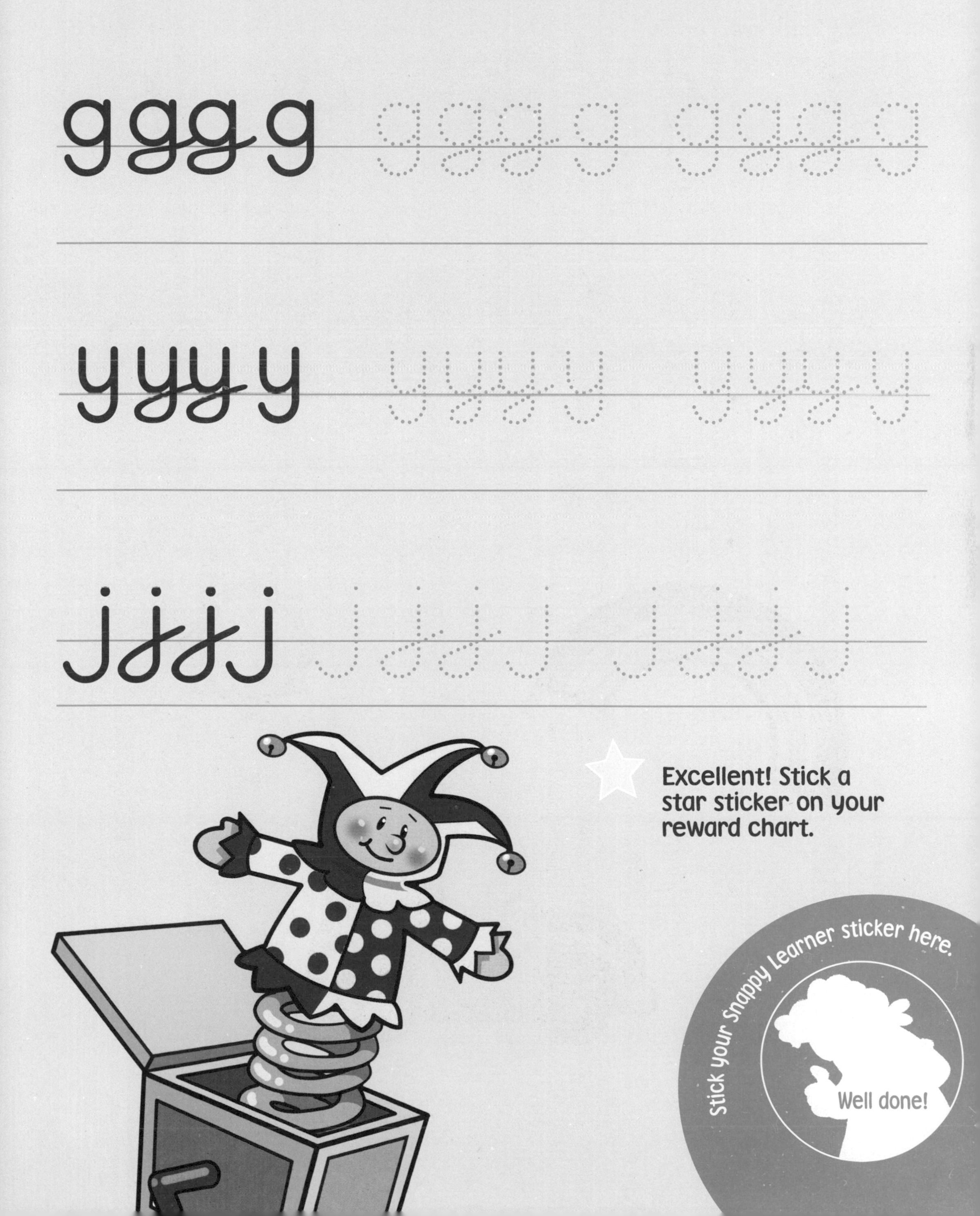

Beginning letters

Copy these letters with their beginning strokes on the line underneath.

Join them up

Trace the letters and add the linking lines to join them up.
Now write them yourself on the line underneath.

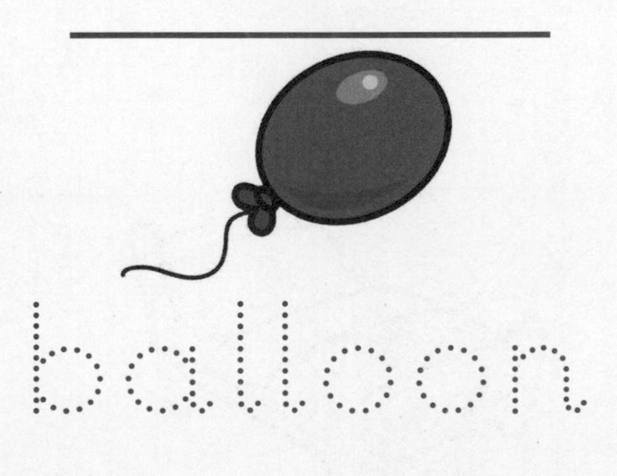

Stick your Snappy Learner sticker here.

Well done!

Excellent! Stick a star sticker on your reward chart.

Capital letters

Write the capital letter at the beginning of each word and join the dotted letters.

Excellent! Stick a star sticker on your reward chart.

Let's write!

Write out these sentences on the lines in joined-up writing. Use the examples to guide you.

a cat and a hat

a cat and a hat

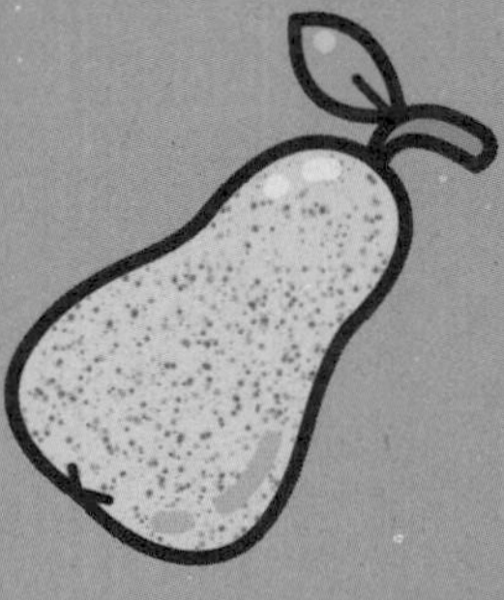

a bear and a pear

a bear and a pear

a moon and a spoon

a moon and a spoon

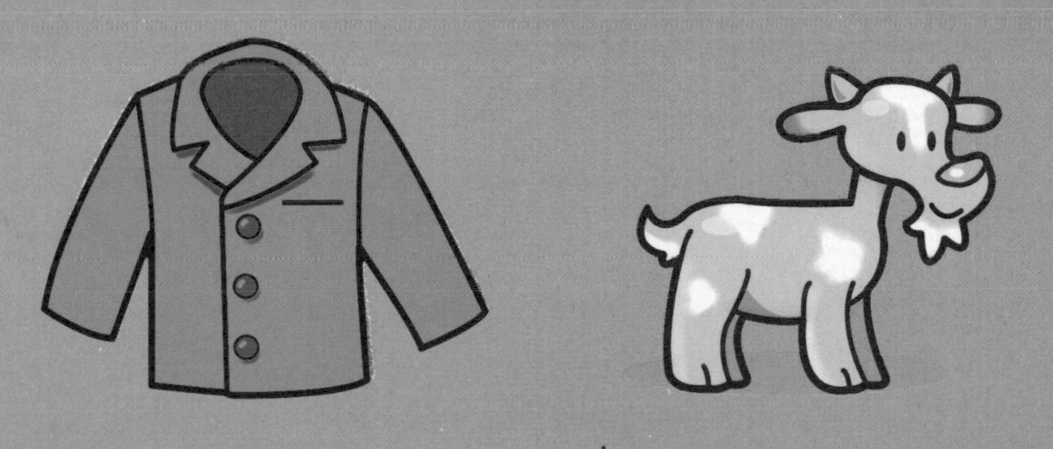

a coat and a goat

a coat and a goat

Excellent! Stick a star sticker on your reward chart.

Write and spell

Spell these words and write the answers on the line underneath in joined-up writing.

Stick your Snappy Learner sticker here.
Well done!
Excellent! Stick a star sticker on your reward chart.

With a capital letter

Write these words starting with a capital letter on the line underneath in joined-up writing. Use the example to guide you.

Excellent! Stick a star sticker on your reward chart.

Let's keep practising!

Write out these sentences on the lines using the examples as a guide. When you have finished, use the last page to write out your own sentences. The more you write, the better you will become!

The lazy dog is sleeping.

Three ducks swimming.
Stick your Snappy Learner sticker here.
Well done!
Excellent! Stick a star sticker on your reward chart.